Zac's Story

by Jan Weeks

illustrated by David Dickson

The Characters

Zac
The new boy
at our school.

Danny
I'm in Zac's class.

Nina
She sits at the desk
in front of me.

Mr McFee
Our teacher.
He's okay.

The Setting

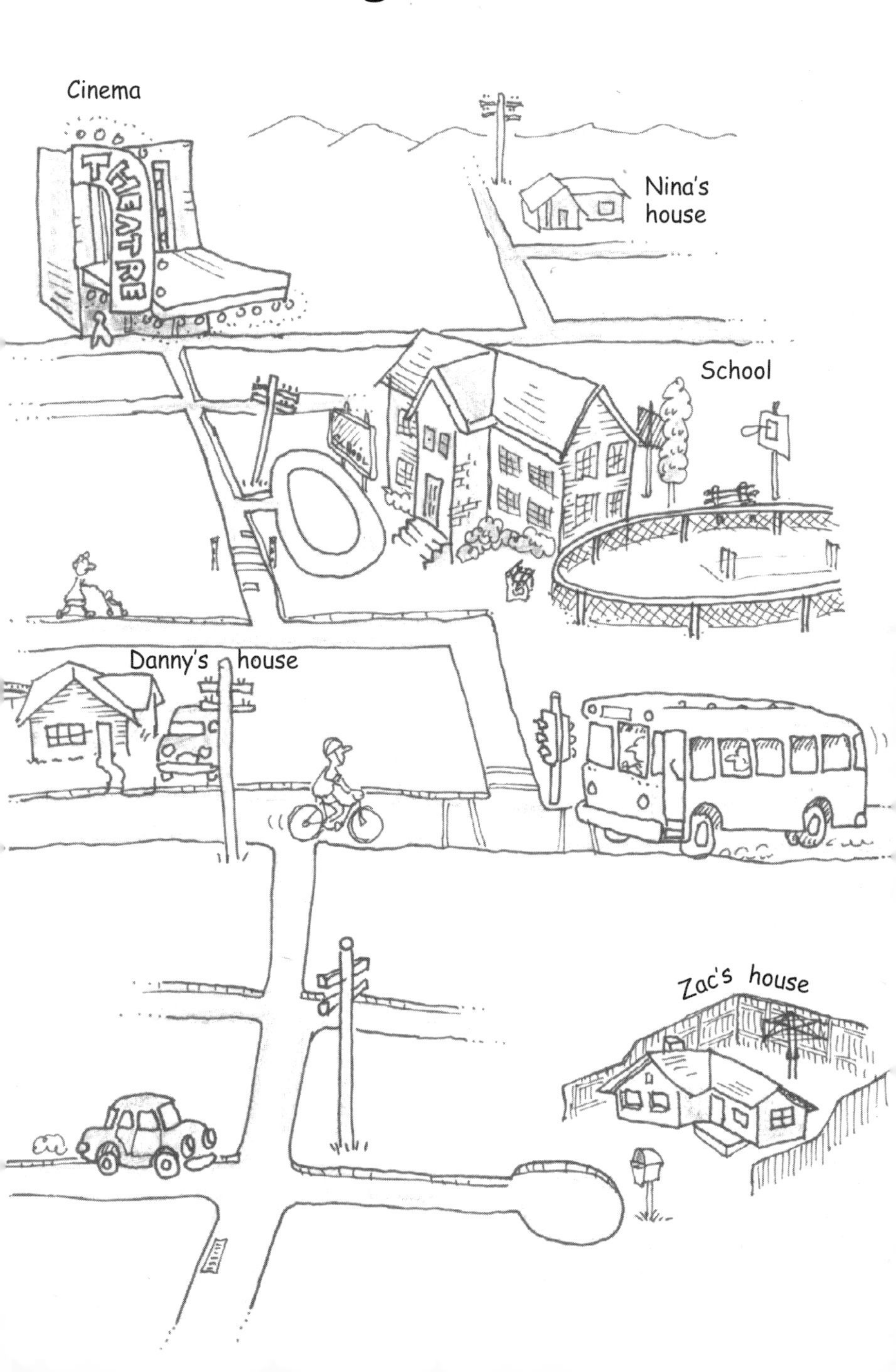

CONTENTS

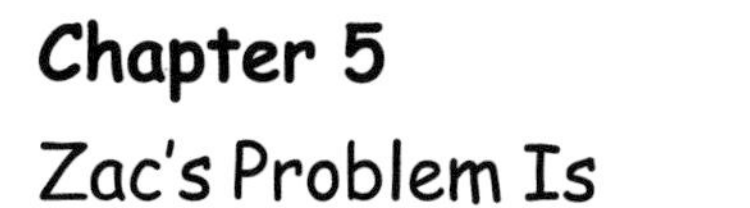

Chapter 1

Zac Changes School Again

Hi! My name is Danny.
I have a new friend, Zac.
He began school today.

"There's no-one sitting in the desk next to me," I said to Mr McFee. I was hoping he'd let Zac sit next to me.

When Mr McFee said he could,
Zac smiled at me. I knew
we were going to be friends.

At lunch time Zac told me he'd been to lots of schools. He didn't stay long in any of them. His mother kept moving.

"Do you like going to new schools?" I asked.

Zac shrugged and said he was used to it.

"I hope you stay here," I said.
I liked Zac. So did Nina.
She sits at the desk in front of us

The next day we all had to take a turn to read.
Mr McFee asked Zac to read aloud.

Zac said he had forgotten to bring his glasses.

"Bring them tomorrow," Mr McFee said.

Zac looked out of the window.

Chapter 2

Zac The Champion

The next day Mr McFee asked Zac if he had his glasses. Zac shook his head.

Zac said he couldn't find them. He said his mother would look for them after work.

"Can't you see without your glasses?" Nina asked.

Zac shook his head.

"Poor Zac," Nina whispered to me. "I hope his mother finds them."

After school, Zac came to my house.
We played games on
my Dad's computer.

Zac could see well enough to play them. He won every game.

Next day our class played cricket. My favourite sports are cricket and rounders.

Only, I'm no good at either.
The other kids groan
when it's my turn to bat.

Mr McFee let Zac be wicket keeper.

When it was my turn to bat
I was out for a duck.

Nina was as well, only it didn't bother her. She laughed and said, "Better luck next time."

Then it was Zac's turn. He hit the ball over the fence. We all yelled "Six!"

"Wow!" Nina and I cried
as we looked at each other.
"What a great batter!"

Mr McFee said Zac should try for the school cricket team.

Zac Gets Into Trouble

Zac's mother took us to the cinema. Nina came as well. Zac told me he wanted to be an actor one day.

Nina thought being a truck driver would be more fun. All I wanted to do was play cricket.

After the film
Zac ran ahead of us.

"Hey Zac!" Nina laughed.
"You're going to the wrong toilet.
That's the Ladies.
Didn't you read the sign?"

Zac's face went red. "No ... no I didn't," he said.

"I did the same thing once," I told him. "Lucky there was nobody in there."

Next day Mr McFee said,
"Have you found your glasses yet, Zac?"
He sounded cross.

Zac had been at school for two week
and hadn't done any work.
I wrote his spelling words in his book
I even had to tell him the answers
to a maths quiz.

Zac said he'd found his glasses but they were broken. His mother was getting them fixed.

Mr McFee looked at Zac.
"You can't learn without your glasses, Zac," he said.

"If you don't bring them tomorrow, I'll write to your mother."

Zac was quiet for the rest of the day.

"I wonder why Zac is making up excuses?" Nina said.

The next day Zac didn't come to school.

Chapter 4

Zac Plays Truant

Nina and I went to Zac's house after school. He was watching a cartoon.

When he saw us he rolled around on the floor. He held his stomach.

"I have a very bad migraine," he said. "Mum's going to take me to the doctor."

He didn't fool us.

"You don't get migraines
in your stomach," Nina told him.
"You get them in your head.
Why didn't you come to school?"

"I'm never going back to that stupid school," Zac said.

I didn't see what his problem was. What was so bad about having to wear glasses? Lots of kids wore glasses. Even Nina.

"I don't have any glasses," said Zac. "I pretend I have to wear them."

"You can't read, can you?" I asked.

Zac shook his head. It was all a bit silly. He should have told Mr McFee.

"I didn't want the others to laugh at me," Zac said. "It's embarrassing not being able to read."

"It'll be more embarrassing when Mr McFee finds out you've been lying and sends you to the Head," said Nina.

Zac's Problem Is Solved

"You're a champion at cricket," I said.

Zac said he'd rather be able to read. He wanted to be an actor. If he couldn't read, how could he learn his lines?

"We'll teach you to read, Zac, and you coach us in cricket. Is it a deal?"

"But you guys are hopeless at cricket,"
ne said with a groan.

"Thanks very much," said Nina.
She didn't really care about cricket
ut she wanted to be part of things.

"Do you really think you could teach me to read?" Zac asked

We nodded. "No problem," we said at the same time.

Zac asked when we would start.

"No time like now," I said.
So we looked for a book.

Who knows what will happen?
With any luck, I could be
a champion cricketer, Zac could be
a famous film star and Nina
could own a fleet of trucks.

embarrassing
to feel shy, uncomfortable
and red faced

excuses
reasons why

fleet
a group of ships,
cars or trucks

groan
a sad low sound

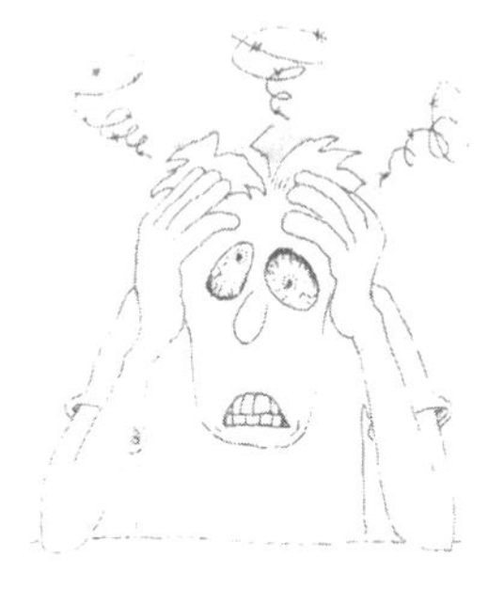

migraine
a bad headache

pretend
something which is
not true

shrugged
moving shoulders up and down;
often means "I don't know
or care."

Jan Weeks

Jan Weeks has written many poems, plays, songs and stories for children. She is an experienced teacher with a particular interest in the development of sound reading skills and the promotion of literature. Jan is married, has three sons and lives in Sydney, Australia.

David Dickson

David Dickson has taught in secondary schools, worked as an education editor for a daily newspaper, a curriculum developer at university, and most recently as publications manager for a research institute. Now he has decided to concentrate on illustration — which is what he should have done all along.